SRA
OPEN COURT
READING

Mom and I

SRA

A Division of The McGraw-Hill Companies

Columbus, Ohio

www.sra4kids.com

SRA/McGraw-Hill

A Division of The **McGraw·Hill** Companies

Send all inquiries to:
SRA/McGraw-Hill
8787 Orion Place
Columbus, OH 43240-4027

ISBN 0-07-569410-7
  2 3 4 5 6 7 8 9 DBH 05 04 03 02

 makes and  .

Mom   toast   jam

 makes  and .

Mom · cereal · juice

 Mom

makes

 cookies

and

 milk .

Mmm !

cookies

I make a  .

card